C000091422

First published 2015 by Modern Toss Ltd.
This edition updated in 2017
Modern Toss, PO Box 386, Brighton BN1 3SN, England
www.moderntoss.com

ISBN 978-0-9564191-7-0

Designed and typeset by Modern Toss
Printed and bound by Spindulys Lithuania

Visit www.moderntoss.com to read more about all our books and to buy them yeah.
You will also find lots of other shit there, and you can sign up to our mailing list so
that you're always kept bang up to date with it, cheers.

MODERN TOSS PRESENTS

Complete Christmas Mood

Cheers

Jon & Mick

by Jon Link and Mick Bunnage

Christmas

seasonal affective disorder

christmas

work

stocking filler

work

festive deal

Christmas

christmas

festive footprint

Mr Tourette

MASTER SIGNWRITER

Oh Hello Mr Tourette I need a sign for my temporary xmas pound shop, I've moved the concept on by allowing people to fill a special bag with as much stuff as they like and it will only cost a pound

very reasonable

Later...

s a bit of a mixed message

yeah, if it wasn't for the fact that we're raking it in, I'd say it was a fucking disaster...

alright if i squeeze in front, i've done 14 pints of lager down the park

SHIT IN A BAG FOR A QUID

well done, as a long term sufferer of Irritable bowel syndrome I'm going to recommend this place on my website www.lastminutepanickshittersinthehighst.com

cheese&wine
All our decorations and cards are totally homemade this year
I wondered why it all looked so fucking shit

yuletide telly

Merry Christmas

Christmas Centrepiece

festive grid drain

would you mind
turning it down a bit,
it's affecting my wife's
dialysis machine

perhaps you'd like
to explain that to my
little kiddie

seasonal work

customer services

seasonal affective disorder

generation gap

awkward cunt

digital seasonal yesteryear

seasonal affective disorder

home~clubber

seasonal pervert

christmas dinner

seasonal cutbacks

business opportunity

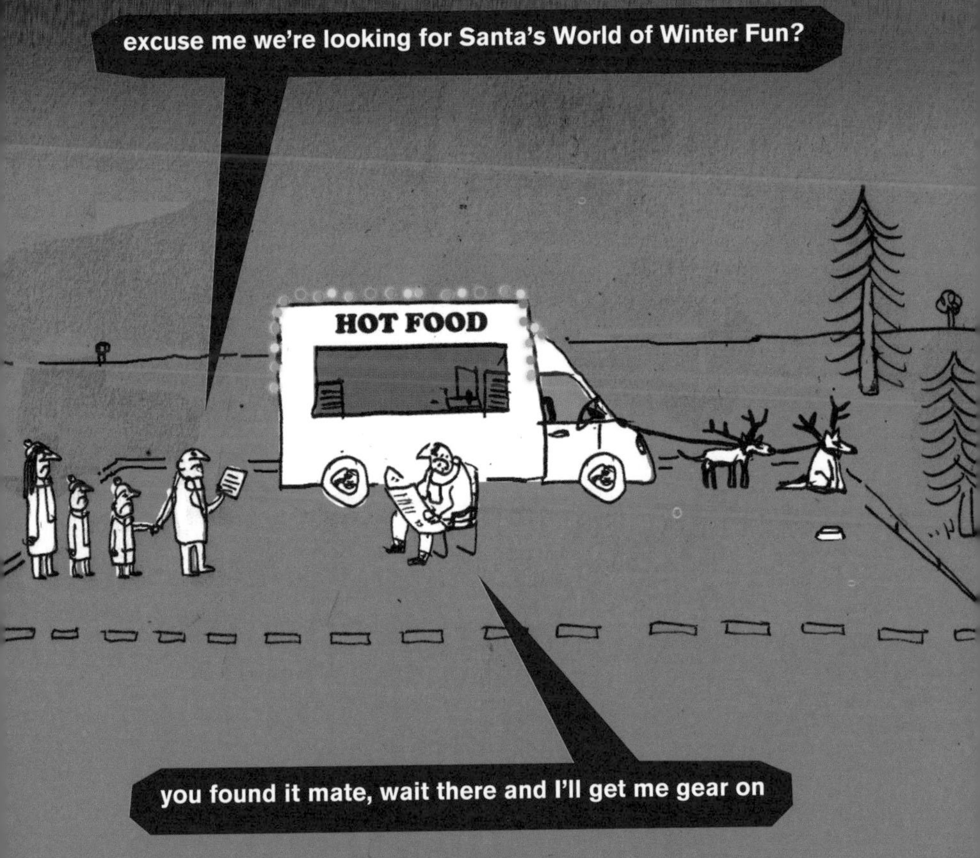

seasonal cutbacks

British Farmers Experimental Turkey Workshop

seasonal affective disorder

stocking filler

yuletide excuse

xmas perfume buyer

desperate shopper

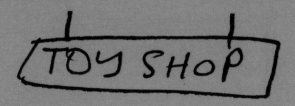

this is the most up to date set, it comes with a replacement bus service

seasonal affective disorder

seasonal affective disorder

British Farmers Experimental Turkey Workshop

drive-by abuser

seasonal tree are you?

pointless existence innit, sitting round like a cunt all year,

then some bloke digs you up and puts you in a bucket

couple of weeks later you're slung out in a bag full of turkey fat

not much of a way to start the new year is it?

DESPERATE BUSINESS

yuletide cutbacks

seasonal affective disorder

office party

you better have more to say for yourself when my parents get here

christmas game

reluctant host

I don't know where Peter's got to but I'll let
him know you popped round, see you next year

food & drink

gift recycler

didn't I give this to you for Christmas

yeah I didn't like it, happy birthday

home~clubber

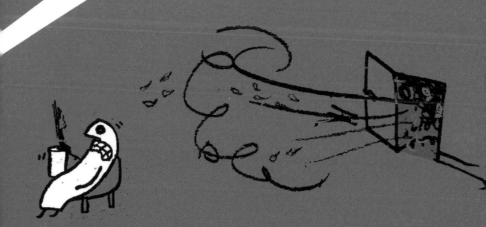

new years arse

work

food & drink

drive-by abuser

alright? waiting for Big Ben to tell you you've just shitted
another year of your life up the fucking wall? yeah why not eh?...